GW00671652

for Tannis

Stripped-back Yoga

Julia Thorley

Namaste,
Julia Thorley.

3P
PUBLISHING

First published in 2018 in the UK

3P Publishing
C E C, London Road
Corby
NN17 5EU

A catalogue number for this book is available
from the British Library

ISBN 978-1-911559-52-8

Cover design: Jamie Rae

Cover painting: Malcolm Parnell
malcolm.parnell3@ntlworld.com

For yoga students everywhere.
The light in me honours the light in you.

Contents:

Introduction

I've been practising yoga since I was a teenager. My first experience was trotting along with my mum to her class, where a roomful of women of a certain age were put through their paces in a community centre by a whippet of a woman in leggings and leotard. My memory of the details is vague – I was there under sufferance, after all – but I don't remember there being a lot of instruction. I think we just followed what was demonstrated. I do, however, remember lying down to relax at the end to the strains of Richard Clayderman. To this day, I can't hear 'Ballade Pour Adeline' without my breathing slowing down.

Anyway, what began as a chore became a pleasure. Over the years, I've tried all sorts of ways to keep fit: gym work, jogging, aerobics, step classes, swimming, trampolining, Zumba, but no matter how far I've strayed from the path I've always gone back to yoga. It was inevitable, I suppose, that I would eventually train to be a teacher. Five hundred long hours and a lot of tears and soul-searching went into my British Wheel of Yoga Diploma. I learned not just about the postures (asana), but also the breathing practices (pranayama), the anatomy and physiology and the philosophy, not to mention actual teaching skills such as how to write and deliver a well-rounded lesson. Despite all this, though, I am essentially still a yoga student with lots of questions unanswered.

What I have put together here is a collection of my thoughts about yoga to be dipped in and out of when you have a couple of minutes to spare. Some of the pieces are about practical aspects of practice; others are a bit ranty because there's a lot about the modern yoga world that rubs my fur the wrong way. For simplicity's sake, I have by and large used English names for the postures, which I'm sure will upset the purists. However, I've retained the Sanskrit for the more esoteric elements, which will no doubt upset some people, too. I haven't deliberately set out to offend anyone, but if I have, well, at least I will have made you think.

Namaste.

Julia Thorley
2018

Caution

This is not an instruction book on how to do yoga. As I am constantly reminding my students, you are responsible for your own wellbeing. You are advised to consult your GP or other medical professional before taking up any new exercise practice and to seek the help and guidance of a qualified teacher.

Let's keep it simple

Yoga is supposed to be a straightforward process. We work our way through Patanjali's eight limbs until we get to *samadhi*. Job done. The trouble is, I'm finding the path increasingly littered with impediments.

It's not that long ago that the only decision we had to make when buying shampoo was whether our hair was normal, dry or greasy. Now there is a bottle for every conceivable variation: straight, curly, frizzy, damaged, coloured, greying, thin, flyaway or brittle: and you can buy shampoo and conditioner, together or separately, and any number of pre- and post-wash lotions and potions for styling. All I want is clean hair. I'm wondering if yoga is going the same way. Are we in danger of being bamboozled by choice and losing sight of what's really important?

The second question that potential new students ask me is usually, 'What sort of yoga do you teach?' I generally answer that I am BWY trained in the hatha tradition, but that I have absorbed elements from various teachers and experiences over the years. (The first question is, 'How much is it?' Rarely does anyone ask me where I trained or even if I'm qualified and insured.)

There seem to be so many different styles of yoga around. Let's start with hatha, ashtanga, Iyengar, kundalini, Dru: the list goes on and is growing. Add in Scaravelli, Bikram and yin, and those that are purely descriptive, such as dynamic, power, restorative, for pregnancy, and trendy ones like barre, aerial and acro – not to mention hybrids like Yogalates and Body Balance – and don't get me started on dog yoga, goat yoga, beer yoga... I'm confused, never mind my students!

There are so many different styles of practice and teaching. You can sign up to this school or that discipline, buy this gadget or that prop, wear this special top and that fab pair of trousers. Don't get me wrong: I'm in favour of choice. All the options out there are needed by someone, but no one needs it all. A teaching style that suits one person doesn't suit another. Props can be a great asset. We need to be comfortably dressed, because no one can focus if her top is forever riding up and her trousers don't sit right. What I am saying is perhaps we should identify the need first and then find the solution. Maybe you want to explore more sequences and flows: who can help you? If you're not confident in inversions, what props could make them more accessible?

So, what sort of yoga do I teach? It depends. I always have a lesson plan but adapt it according to who turns up and how we're all feeling. Sometimes we work really slowly, sometimes more dynamically. Sometimes we have a very precise class, but sometimes we're more mellow, and we just go with the flow, literally and metaphorically. Sometimes the age of my students on the night means it's an over-50s session. Other times the boiler is playing up and we inadvertently have hot yoga.

I don't want or need a specific label on my classes. What I deliver is 'Julia's yoga', whatever that is. In the end, there is asana, pranayama and meditation. Let's keep it simple.

The long road to perfection

I do yoga, so I'm perfect. I only eat organic food, I don't drink alcohol, I never lose my temper, and I always see the best in everyone and everything. *Not!*

I was having one of those days when I'd tumbled out of bed and barely had time to wash and dress before settling down at my computer to earn a living. I knew, though, that supplies were running low, so mid-morning I thought I'd sneak a quick trip to the supermarket. I ran a comb through my hair, put on a slick of lippy, checked that my clothes were at least respectable and set off.

Any other day I would have been there and back without seeing anyone I knew, but not that day. Serves me right for being slovenly, I suppose. I was browsing amongst the yoghurts when I heard a voice behind me:

'Julia? I thought it was you! What are you doing here? I thought you had moral objections to supermarkets!'

It was one of the women from the edge of my circle: not really a friend, but more than just an acquaintance, and always beautifully turned out.

I forced a smile and a cheery reply: 'It's just a quick dash out and back for a few basics.'

'Are you OK? You look rather drawn,' she continued. Her disapproval of my dishevelled appearance was evident.

'Fine, thanks, but I can't stop. Probably see you by the pasta.' I laughed feebly and made my escape.

I hadn't gone much further when I bumped into a former student. My heart sank as I watched her eyes take in the contents of my trolley: wine, instant noodles and chocolate. I fought the desire to explain that while, yes, the wine was mine, it was a treat; and the junk was for my son who despite my best efforts likes to balance my nutritious home-cooked offerings with a regular input of salt and sugar. Anyway, the bottom layer of the trolley was filled with healthy stuff, honestly. So much for leading by example.

It's all very well if you live in an ashram beyond the reach of temptation, but out here in the real world we face the constant challenge of avoiding what we know is bad for us and making positive, life-enhancing choices. Let's not beat ourselves up about it. I'm not perfect; I'm a work in progress.

Insert serene smile here.

Yoga practice?
It's all in a day's work

Practising yoga doesn't mean you have to be fanatical. You don't have to rise at dawn, roll out your mat and go through a gruelling two-hour routine. With a little imagination and focus, you can slot in your practice throughout your day. I warn you now, this is going to sound rather sanctimonious. Try to smile as you read it.

Even before you get out of bed, in that hazy, coming-round state, take a moment to see how you feel. Take a slow, deep breath in and raise your arms overhead as you have a good stretch. Scrunch up your fingers and toes, then spread them as wide as you can. Rotate your ankles and wrists. Turn your head gently from one side to the other, then tuck your chin down to lengthen the back of your neck.

There you are: that's yoga before you've even opened your eyes!

Down into the kitchen you go for breakfast. Sneak in a few mini-postures while you're waiting for the kettle to boil and the toaster to pop. Hold on to the edge of your worktop and walk your feet away until your back is long and flat. Straighten your legs. Hey presto: flank stretch! (How are your hamstrings today?) The more adventurous of you – subject to space and a tolerant household – might want to rest a foot on a chair or even on the sink and bend forwards to bring your nose towards your knee.

Reaching up to get the marmalade, can you work in a lateral stretch? If the jar is in the left-hand cupboard, use your right hand to reach up and across your body. Need milk? Don't plant your feet and bend forwards stiffly. Instead, rise up on your toes, then soften your knees and, with your body upright, drop down into a squat, retrieve the carton, then reverse the process to come up again.

Once you are up and dressed, it's off to the bus stop or into your car. How's your posture? Spine alert, neck long and shoulders relaxed?

As you reach for your seatbelt or turn your head to see what's behind you, take the opportunity to work in a spinal rotation. Before you move, breathe in and lengthen your spine, and as you turn, consciously rotate your spine – and not just your neck. Having twisted one way, remember to rotate the other way, too, to keep your body balanced.

If you get stuck in a traffic jam, there's nothing you can do about it, so take the opportunity to check your posture and breathing. Unclench your teeth, give your arms and legs a shake, roll your shoulders back and take some proper breaths, breathing in deeply from your abdomen up to the top of your chest and out again. If you're feeling agitated, focus on lengthening your out-breath to slow everything down. Apply slight abdominal tone to bring in your core muscles.

Actually, it's well worth doing this spot check regularly throughout the day. Take yourself to the toilets, if that's the only place at work you can be sure you'll get a minute's peace. If necessary, programme your phone to beep every hour or so to remind you to do this.

OK, so you park the car or get off the bus. As you walk into work, keep your stride even and let your arms swing freely at your sides. If you have a laptop or other stuff to carry, don't always drape it over the same shoulder. Vary the load to avoid bad habits and don't forget about keeping your body balanced.

If you sit at a desk, don't lean on the back of your chair without using a cushion in the small of your back to support your spine. The chair back is for putting your jacket on, not for holding you up. Again, think about your core muscles. Place your feet flat on the floor – stick a book under them, if you have to – to keep your pelvis level. Set up your desk space so you have to reach for things: great chance for a stretch. Put your bin behind you, so you can bring in a spinal rotation, alternating the way you turn, of course.

When you stand up to leave your work station, bring your fists into the small of your back, push your pelvis forwards (discretely, if you share an office), draw your shoulders back to open your chest and you've got yourself a back bend. You can get a similar effect if you clasp your hands behind you, straighten your arms and pull back your shoulders.

If you are on your feet all day, bring yourself into Tadasana (standing up straight in Mountain Pose) whenever you can. Your legs will thank you for it. You might think you are giving your right leg a rest when you transfer your weight to your left leg and sink down into one hip, but all you're actually doing is unbalancing your pelvis and your spine. Perhaps when no one's looking, you could even go up on to tiptoes (breathing in) and down again (breathing out).

You've survived another day at work. All that stands in the way between you and your evening is a trawl round the supermarket, but take heart: this will offer you plenty of opportunities for bending and stretching, lengthening and rotating.

One of the most useful yoga techniques here is surely your breathing. Keep it deep, slow and even, and focus on your out-breath to stop your stress levels rising – or how about a touch of *ujjayi* breathing (Victory Breath) to give you the strength to carry on? I wouldn't recommend *bhramari* pranayama (Humming Bee Breath), unless you want to attract the attention of the security staff.

If you favour a basket – and let's face it, you spend less if you only buy what you can carry – change hands as you go, and if your back starts to tug, you need either to put something back on the shelf or to switch to a trolley.

Speaking of which, a trolley is for holding your goods; it is not a walking frame. Look about you at your fellow shoppers: how many of them push their trolley in a stoop, with their forearms resting on the handle and their bum sticking out inelegantly behind? Fingertip control is all that's needed to steer your way around the aisles. It's back to posture again.

You glide your way round in a cocoon of tranquillity and join the queue at the checkout. You've already got your posture and your breathing under control. Now, what else can you do?

You could perhaps apply *mula bandha* (base lock), if you can focus on your pelvic floor muscles without crossing your eyes. Or how about a concentration exercise? Watch the checkout operator. Note the colour of his hair, whether he is wearing any jewellery, how he moves, how he sounds. Take care, though, not to stare too intently. When he comes to serve you, does he look at you? Does he smile? (Do you?) This is a non-judgemental exercise in observation, not an opportunity for finding fault.

Back at home, you put away your shopping, again taking every chance to bend, stretch, lengthen and rotate.

While you cook your supper and are waiting for something to come to the boil or for microwave to work its magic, pop in a quick balance – well away from the lit hob, just in case – perhaps Dancer, or even a basic quad stretch, standing on one leg and holding the other bent behind you as you feel a stretch in the muscles in the front of your thigh.

Time to watch a bit of TV, then, but think before you slump down in your favourite armchair. What other position could you adopt? Perhaps crossed legs or soles together in Cobbler, or stretch your legs away in Staff Pose, or legs crossed beneath you and knees stacked as for the Cow's Head posture, alternating sides, of course; or you could go to extremes, sit with the TV behind you and use a seated spine twist. OK, so I'm joking now, but you get the idea.

With a little thought about your day, you can easily incorporate yoga. It's about being mindful, without turning into a yoga prima donna, making flamboyant gestures at every turn and wearing a smug smile.

Adopt and adapt these suggestions. Explore the possibilities and who knows: you might find you are mopping the floor to the rhythm of Hari Om!

Are you sitting comfortably?

You might be at your desk and desperate for a good stretch to relieve the tension in your body; perhaps you have broken your ankle and are temporarily incapacitated, or maybe illness or disability means that your movement is restricted. Whatever the reason, there is always a way to work with what you've got. What follows are not step-by-step instructions, but rather suggestions on how you can modify your yoga for a seated practice.

Always think about your safety. If your chair has wheels, make sure you put the brakes on or wedge it securely. Check that you have room around you to move your arms freely. If possible, you should be able to plant your feet firmly on the floor (or use a block), so that your pelvis is level and you can sit with an erect spine. If you're in the office, take off your high heels!

Just as you would in a conventional practice, take a moment to settle yourself before you start. Check that you have an upright posture. Don't lean into the back of your chair or rest on its arms; it is your muscles that should be holding you up.

Rotate your head gently from side to side and release any tension in your neck, then bring your shoulders forward, up, back and down, drawing them away from your ears so that your neck is long. Close your eyes, bring your attention to your breathing and allow your body to settle.

To warm up, clench and stretch your hands, shrug and move your shoulders, rotate your ankles and wriggle your toes, and generally explore how your body is feeling. Focus on the movement you have, rather than the limitations.

An all-over yoga practice should take your spine through its full range of movement. Let's think about forward bends. If your lower body is stable, it is relatively easy to accomplish this sitting down. Pulling in your core muscles to protect your back, let your arms hang by your sides, breathe in as you bring your arms over your head, then as you breathe out let your body move forwards so your hands can go down to your feet. With your chest supported on your thighs, you can really let go in this position.

When you bring yourself upright, counterpose with a back arch. Take your hands behind you and hold on to the back edge of your chair seat. Draw your shoulder blades together and lift your chest towards the ceiling. Take your head back, too, if it's comfortable, but don't hyperextend or there is a risk of damage to your neck.

You could intensify this stretch by clasping your hands behind you and straightening your arms, or hold one end of a strap in each hand behind your head with your arms straight, and gradually walk your hands towards each other, which takes your shoulders back and encourages your chest to open. Alternatively, try pressing into your feet and lifting your bum off the chair to increase the arch.

A sideways bend can be achieved by resting your right hand on the chair arm or holding the edge of the seat, and then bringing your left arm up and alongside your ear until you feel some work in your oblique muscles and a lovely stretch along the whole of your left side. Don't forget to work both sides equally.

There are many conventional seated rotations, so doing them in a chair is a fairly straightforward transition. Observe that if you hold your arms out at shoulder height with your palms facing forwards and keep your legs still as you rotate, you will end up in virtually the same position as you would in a simple lying twist.

Vary the position of your arms to see which is best for you. You can also modify the movement by crossing your right leg over your left as you rotate to the right. Bring your head into the movement, too, if it is comfortable for your neck.

When it comes to balances, simply lifting your feet off the ground without using your hands to steady yourself can focus the mind. Then vary it by extending one leg or both legs out in front of you, in the style of the Boat posture.

Alternatively, while balancing a book on your head might sound like an old-school deportment exercise, it is still valid, particularly if you then turn your head from side to side. Or try this: extend your hand and perch a coin on the pad of your little finger. Now without using your other hand, transfer that coin to the next finger, and the next, all the way to your thumb, and back. Now change hands.

Next, take yourself into a gentle but effective inversion. If you're able to get out of your chair, lie on the floor so that you can rest your feet on the seat, putting your arms wherever they are comfortable. Alternatively, if you want or need to stay seated, lean back into your chair using cushions and blankets to support you as necessary, then bring your feet up in front of you on to another chair, raising them up on blocks or cushions as high as is comfortable.

Finish your practice with a breath focus exercise, then ease yourself into your meditation or relaxation, knowing that you are safe and comfortable in your chair.

Make full use of props to explore ways to develop your chair yoga. In a rotation, you can use the arms or back of the chair to encourage your body to twist a little further. Using belts and straps anchored firmly around another chair or working with a partner, you can pull yourself deeper into postures, but with the security that you can let go at any time if you feel you are going too far – great for forward bends or lengthening in the spine. Hook a belt around the sole of your foot and then let the belt take the weight so you can to coax that leg straight and work on lengthening the hamstrings. Having something to hold on to can be reassuring and give you the confidence to explore, knowing that you are not going to topple over.

Even if you don't have to work in a chair, it is an interesting experience and can bring an extra dimension to your practice. You might think you are sitting up straight, for example, but if you sit on the edge of your chair without leaning on the back or arms for support, it can really bring home how soft your posture is. It might come as a surprise to discover just how slumped you are until you consciously straighten yourself out. With your sitting bones in contact with your chair, it is easier to discern where your weight is distributed and how it shifts when you move. Consider, for instance, whether when you work in lateral movements you 'cheat' by lifting one buttock so that your body can lean over further than it might otherwise do.

As with all yoga, you need to be conscious of all the precautions and prohibitions that usually apply and to be mindful of your own physical and mental wellbeing; and remember: just because it's not a classical asana with a Sanskrit name doesn't mean it's not yoga.

Hip hurray for the NHS!

The patient looks anxiously from the doctor to the consultant and sees them exchange a knowing look. 'May I speak to you for a moment?' one says to the other.

They step outside of the cubicle to discuss the likely outcome, as though that thin blue curtain somehow creates a soundproof wall. Well, this might work on TV, but not in real life.

When my mother was in hospital for a mercifully short stay for a hip replacement (she's doing fine, thanks for asking), I perched uncomfortably at her bedside in a bay holding four ladies. The idea that the flimsy curtains afford any privacy is optimistic, but to think that they can provide a barrier to eavesdropping is simply unrealistic.

I tried not to listen, honestly, I did, but I was only feet away from the next bed, which makes it impossible not to overhear what follows the request for the bedpan. Comments such as, 'It's no good, there's nothing happening,' and 'Is that all you can manage?' are not meant to be shared with strangers. Then there are those 'procedures' that go on behind the drapes. I'm not sure which is worse: speculating what's underneath the cloth carried in on that nasty steel tray and what is brought out, or wondering exactly what is being revealed in response to the command: 'Just a bit wider for me, please, Elsie.'

Any of my family will tell you that I'm not a good nurse. Despite being an avid fan of *House* ('It's never lupus') and *Casualty* (He's in VF!') and quite the armchair diagnostician, my idea of nursing is to keep asking, 'Do you feel better yet?' So, I'm a big fan of not only the medical professionals, but also the support staff. Many years ago, in another life, I worked in an NHS personnel department, as it was called then, and was involved in creating training courses for hospital porters. Many of the things they are expected to do for the living and the dead beggar belief!

When a poorly friend or relative needs help, some of us are better at doing the shopping, tidying round and putting in washing than changing dressings and holding the emesis bowl. I know where I stand (well away from the messy end), but I'm so grateful that there are people who feel called to care for the sick. My contribution is to spread the yoga message to help my students stay healthy.

Let's hear it for the boys!

In all the years that I have been practising yoga, I have always found classes and, latterly, professional events predominantly female affairs. Yoga was devised by and for men, so where are they all?

My experience leads me to infer that many more women than men are drawn to yoga. Why is this? Is it the misconception that yoga is easy and a little bit girly? Or, conversely, is it that men are more afraid than women of revealing their weaknesses in public? Might it be that the thought of not being able to hold a posture the longest of anyone in the room is not an option? Is it simply that yoga isn't promoted to men in the media and by yoga associations? Do they fear being the only male in the room? Are there any yoga posters in the male changing rooms in your local sports club?

There are, of course, plenty of men out there enjoying their yoga for all sorts of reasons. Plumber Jay practises yoga at home because it keeps him flexible enough to squeeze into tight spaces and then gives him the tools he needs to ease out after a physical day's work. However, he's never been to a formal class.

He says, 'I just don't fancy it.'

Yet his belief in the benefits of yoga extends to the point where, wearing his other hat as a coach of a youth football team, he encourages his players to do some yoga postures as part of their pre-training warm-up.

He's not alone here. I was approached by my local semi-professional football team to draw up a programme of yoga for the squad, because the manager felt that although his players were fit and strong, they needed more balance and focus in their approach to matches and that yoga would help them to concentrate.

I have found that the men who come to the classes I teach tend to have a specific reason for taking up yoga, rather than a general belief that it will do them good all over. Often it is because a medical professional has suggested it would help them overcome an injury or will help them to de-stress, or because it will complement other aspects of their fitness regime and lifestyle. Rick, for instance, does a lot of long-distance running, but likes to attend a yoga class to help him stretch out tight leg muscles.

Sometimes they are there because they have been dragged along by their partner. Charles originally took up yoga at the suggestion of his wife. As they are both competitive sportspeople, it was a way they could attend a physical class together without coming to blows! But Charles didn't take to it. He found being the only man in the class made him rather self-conscious, but that wasn't the real issue.

He explains: 'I didn't find it particularly demanding, but probably because I wasn't executing the moves to their full extent. After a few weeks, doing the same postures, again and again, became

22

boring for me. I like aerobic exercise, in particular, one-on-one games with a ball, and while I found the yoga experience interesting, ultimately it just wasn't rewarding.'

Despite his rather negative view, Charles does concede that in later life the undoubted improved flexibility that yoga brings might be worth pursuing.

Nor is it just the physical aspects of yoga that appeal to the men, any more than to women. Lewis was drawn to it as part of a major overhaul of his life. Following some personal and emotional decluttering, he gave up smoking, improved his diet, started to take regular exercise, lost weight and changed his job in order to escape the stress of a long daily commute, but he still felt there was something missing. He saw yoga as a means to develop a spiritual side alongside some gentle exercise.

He says, 'I soon realised that yoga was much more than [the physical]. Today, I practise asana for at least an hour each day, I meditate, I read books and magazines on the subject, I attend two classes each week and various seminars and courses. I look to yoga as the foundation for building my life and to provide structure for my thoughts.'

At the gym where I teach, new members often try every class going to find what suits them, so occasionally I have men turning up who wouldn't dream of going to a 'proper' yoga class. Some are surprised at how tough it can be; others find the lack of a competitive element difficult and don't understand why I tell them to stop if it hurts. Most stay to the end, but there are exceptions.

One chap made his discomfort very clear right from the start. His verbal and body language made it obvious that he wasn't at all happy. He told me he was into strong cardiovascular workouts and that his muscles were probably quite tight as a result. He lasted fifteen minutes into the hour before announcing that yoga wasn't for him, rolling up his mat and leaving. Well, at least he gave it a try, and who knows: one day he may come back.

My least successful attempt at teaching so far has been with a man who turned up at a taster session, again at a gym. He wouldn't take his shoes off, didn't listen and generally huffed and puffed his way through the whole class. He clearly hated it and wasn't shy about making his feelings known.

At the end, he told me, 'That was rubbish. Yoga isn't proper exercise.'

I forced a smile and reminded myself that you can't teach people what they're not ready to learn, whatever their gender.

Gym bunny or yoga babe?

On the face of it, working out in a gym would seem to be the antithesis of all things yoga: the attachment to working harder for longer, for lifting heavier weights and running greater distances on the treadmill in a shorter time – not to mention the ego trip when others stop work before we do or we have to crank up the weights before taking over a machine. Yoga is about working with your body, not against it. We strive always to be steady and comfortable, not to sweat and strain until we feel ready to drop.

Do these two approaches to health and fitness have to be mutually exclusive? Why can't we find a way to do both?

I have friends who love going to the gym, but say yoga doesn't appeal to them because it doesn't make them push themselves to the limit. It's as though if they don't come home exhausted they don't feel they've had a proper workout. Then there is the competitive element. Gyms tend to set their members targets as a way of monitoring their progress and as motivation to encourage them to keep coming back. There's nothing wrong with this, of course. If the carrot of dropping a dress size or the stick of failure is what gets you off the sofa, that's fine. I completely understand why the ethos of yoga might not strike a chord with you.

Most people would agree that a comprehensive yoga practice improves all-round strength and flexibility and results in a toned body, and that it is a great way to relieve stress and relax. However, one criticism that is often levelled at it is that it doesn't help with weight loss or give much of a cardiovascular workout; they should try 108 rounds of Salute to the Sun.

On the other hand, there are many yogis who have never set foot inside a gym and have no intention of doing so. Why they say, would I want to come away from a class feeling more exhausted than when I went in? And what about all those TV screens and the relentless *boom, boom, boom*? How am I supposed to find a point of stillness? Not to mention the mirrors!

Maybe there are valid points on both sides of the argument. I don't like running: it hurts my knees and shakes up my insides; but I do like a brisk swim to get my blood racing and my heart pumping strongly. I also enjoy frenetic dancing (when no one's looking), which is surely the cousin of aerobics or dance fitness like Zumba or SOSA. Does that mean I'm going against my yoga principles? I don't think it does. One of the best teachers I know is an avid fan of electronic dance music, and I shall always be a rock chick at heart. Conversely, doesn't everyone sometimes just want to sit and be, even if they don't call it relaxation or meditation?

I have learnt that what suits my conventional hatha yoga community classes isn't always going to sit well with sessions I run in gyms. My gym students sign up for a class for all sorts of reasons: they might already be practising yoga, or have heard it's good for stretching tight hamstrings, or they might just fancy having a go. A steep learning curve has taught me that, unlike a regular weekly yoga class where I build up a connection with my students, in a gym you never know who is going to turn up. However, they generally have two things in common: they don't want to sit about contemplating their navel – and in any case, it is often a bit chilly in a studio more suited to energetic exercise classes – and they don't want any overt philosophy. At least, that's what they think when they first come along...

The simple fact that gym members even contemplate yoga must mean that there is room for both. So, am I perhaps under some professional or moral obligation to try to introduce the full yoga package and not just the asanas? After all, that is what I'm qualified to teach. Or is that condescending, implying that I know what's best? I don't want to alienate anyone, but at the same time I'd like to hint at what else yoga has to offer besides the physical postures. I give postures their Sanskrit names, where appropriate, and emphasise the connection between body, breath and mind. I bring in elements of yoga philosophy. No doubt some people have gone away dissatisfied, but many return.

For many years, I worked with a wonderful teacher who embodied everything that comes to mind when you think of yoga. She was kind and patient, generous with her time and her possessions, energetic on every level, open-hearted and, crucially, open-minded. I attended a series of workshops of hers that combined yoga with salsa and street dance, working with weights and even some kickboxing moves. Far from this detracting from the serious business of asana and pranayama, I was enthused by what she showed us, and while I wasn't tempted to stray from the path, as it were, it did open my eyes to ways of livening things up. Moving in and out of a Warrior posture with a 2kg weight in each hand really focuses the mind! And it works.

I knew what to expect when I signed up for these workshops. I might have been surprised, to say the least, if I had gone to what I was expecting to be yoga and been handed a set of dumbbells at the door. Working this way showed me that just because I am a yoga teacher it doesn't mean I can't explore other fitness options.

Over the years, whatever else I've been doing in my personal fitness regime, I've always used yoga as the foundation. The two approaches can work together, but maybe like any partnership, we need to try hard to make things work and not be afraid to try something a little different to keep things fresh.

And if that means doing a yoga flow to Justin Bieber, why not?

Laugh and the world laughs with you

There was an audible groan when the team leader uttered those fateful words: icebreaker activity. I don't know if it's a peculiarly British trait, but none of us seems comfortable being forced – sorry, encouraged – to shake hands with a stranger or engage in some 'fun' bit of business to break down barriers and create feelings of teamwork.

Over the years, I've been asked to wear a badge identifying me as Mitchell and been told to find Webb, while elsewhere in the room Tom sought out Jerry, Ant found Dec, and Marge found Homer. I have climbed through hoops, literally and figuratively, I've clapped out a rhythm to be passed round the room and played Chinese whispers. Oh, how we laughed!

This time, however, it was a bit different. It was a non-yoga event, but the icebreaker was laughter yoga. There was, perhaps predictably, some opposition to both laughter and yoga from some quarters, but I was relieved. I'd done this before.

Rainbow Rosie beamed at us and steamrollered on with her task, seemingly oblivious to the reluctance of certain people to join in. We experimented with different styles of laughing: are you a hee-hee person or a ho-ho-ho-er? Do you laugh from your belly or from somewhere high in your sinuses? We put a chuckle in a box and passed it round the room; we shared the hilarity of a bar bill ('Look at these prices. They're having a laugh.'); we lay down on the floor and felt the vibration of our guffaws transfer from our bodies to the carpet.

Rainbow Rosie persevered, and by the end of the session everyone was joining in to some degree. I loved it, but I can understand why some people didn't. I was in a good mood before we started, but I can imagine that if I'd had a bad journey in or had something troubling me, the last thing I'd want is some dippy hippy telling me to laugh it all away.

Actually, this was something that Rosie addressed. She suggested that even if we didn't feel like laughing, we should pretend that we did: 'Fake it, fake it, until you make it!' I could relate to this. Much as I love my students, there are some days when I don't feel like sharing the yoga joy and have to paint on a smile.

So, the next time you feel a grouch coming on, turn it into a giggle. It might sound insincere in your head, but to the outside world, you will look like a positive, happy person. Try it: it works.

Laughing out loud.

Up close and personal

Who needs a one-to-one yoga session? Sure, the rich and famous can justify it on the grounds that they don't want the world and his wife staring at them in a public class or taking pictures for the internet. What about the rest of us? Surely, we, too, would benefit from a private lesson or two.

It might surprise you to learn that quite a lot of people who ask for a one-to-one session are beginners. Often, they want to get a few basic postures and a bit of terminology under their belt before venturing into a general class, or they might simply want to find out a bit more about yoga (and the teacher) before committing to a course.

Others like the security and discretion that a private lesson affords if they are shy or lacking in confidence and therefore uncomfortable in a general class. Others still might have health considerations that make a group session inappropriate. Some just prefer to have a teacher come to them so that they are in a familiar and comfortable environment.

Yogis returning to practice after a break sometimes book a one-to-one session to refresh their knowledge and also for the insight it brings into their physical, emotional and spiritual condition.

While it is lovely to be able to go to a yoga class on a regular basis to support our personal, home-based practice, this simply isn't possible for everyone. If you have a complicated home or work life and find it difficult to commit to a regular class, booking ad hoc private lessons can be an invaluable way to keep up your practice in a way that is better suited to your lifestyle.

Even if you are attending a regular class, a one-to-one can still be beneficial if, say, you need a bit of a boost to your motivation. This is also true for those who practise alone; in fact, they may well be in greater need of inspiration.

Experienced yogis might book a one-to-one session:

- To work through questions about a specific asana – for example, ways to approach the challenges of Scorpion
- To explore in depth a particular aspect of yoga that isn't covered in their general class, such as chanting or yoga philosophy
- To establish, develop or update a personal practice
- If they feel they are not receiving sufficient adjustment or attention from their teacher in a class situation – the personalising of the teaching is a key factor for many private students
- To explore a different branch of yoga or teaching style
- As a treat – for the cost of a decent haircut, you could find your yoga practice kick-started, revitalised and re-energised

Whatever your reasons for booking a one-to-one session, it is useful to have an idea of what you want to achieve, so that you don't waste valuable time when you get there. Beware, though, that while it is good to have a goal in mind, you will still need to discuss your objectives with your teacher so that you can decide between you the best way to proceed. Be prepared to be flexible, because although ultimately the programme has to lead to the results you seek, talking it through might reveal aspects of yoga that you hadn't considered – and this applies whether you are a newbie or an old hand.

You need to be sure that your expectations and those of the teacher are the same, and to say if you're not happy. A good yoga teacher won't take it personally if you simply don't like his or her style and may well be able to point you towards someone else better suited to your needs and way of learning.

Be honest and don't be coy. There is no use pretending that you are ultra-flexible if you can't sit with your legs crossed or saying you exercise regularly if you get out of breath in Tadasana. Be prepared to accept and act on feedback.

A one-to-one session can be a one-off, but it is likely that you will need more. The first session can be primarily a discussion, coupled with an assessment of your level of practice, health, etc, and the setting of a programme for you to work on before you meet again. Session two will allow you to review this programme and to adjust it, depending on progress. Session three should see you reviewing progress again and settling on the way to proceed. This might well be enhanced with follow-up sessions.

If your teacher doesn't ask about your health and any medical conditions during your initial consultation, you might be better to try elsewhere. Yoga teachers aren't doctors, but they should be aware of the anatomical and physiological implications of any practice they suggest, and this should include knowledge of the associated prohibitions and precautions.

One-to-one sessions can be held in your home, the teacher's home or studio or somewhere else. Be sensible. Both parties should let someone know where they will be and what time they are expected home. Arrange to give someone a quick text at the end of the session, so they know all went well. You could even take a chaperone if you are unsure. Personal recommendation is often the best option.

The real benefit of a one-to-one session is that it can be tailored precisely to your needs. The individual attention you receive means that your asana can be tweaked and fine-tuned to suit your proportions and range of movement. Even in the best-planned group class, sometimes it just won't suit how you are feeling that day.

And setting aside the yoga resistance to ego, for a moment, isn't it nice to be the centre of attention for a while?

You wear it well

Age is a funny business. When we're children, we want to be taken for older than we are. Remember those milestones: double figures and then, finally, those longed-for teenage years? We flushed with pride when someone said, 'You look so grown-up.'

At some point, perhaps as the laughter lines start gathering at the corners of the eyes, we start to deny the passage of time. We want people to think that we are younger than we are – or, failing that, to be told we look good for our age. The thing is, of course, that most of us are wearing well (especially we yogis, she adds, modestly).

I don't know if it is improvements in lifestyle or simply changing expectations, but if you look at photos from the Edwardian era, everyone seemed like a pensioner. It's as though there were no degrees of adulthood. Once you were married and had fulfilled your role by ensuring the family line continued for another generation, that was it. You put your hair in a bun, wrapped a rug around your knees and waited for it all to end.

Somewhere along the way, we switch from focusing on youth to wearing our age like a trophy. We all know an old lady who says with pride, 'I'm eighty-eight, you know!' Not in a way that implies we are meant to make allowances for her, just the opposite: we are expected to respond with incredulity.

The young and the old are allowed to speak as they find. I remember very clearly taking a bus trip with my then toddler son when an overweight man got on, huffing and squeezing his way into a seat. No one said anything, except my son.

At the top of his voice, he observed: 'What a piggy!'

I don't teach yoga to very young children anymore, it's just not my thing; but I've served my time in classrooms and know from harsh experience that youngsters don't hold back when it comes to verbalising their observations. They're quick to point out when they don't like what they're being asked to do. I've also done quite a bit of teaching in care homes. On one memorable occasion, one of the elderly residents was less than impressed. After about five minutes she'd had enough.

'I'm going back to my room,' she declared. 'This is just getting on my nerves.' Bless her for her honesty.

One of the joys of yoga is that you can't be too young or too old. Let's not get hung up on the numbers, but instead let's celebrate what we can do, whatever it says on the calendar.

Wrinkles show where the smiles have been

It was clear from the moment we opened the door that there was no heating on in the church room that day. The caretaker couldn't be roused, so I gave the ladies the choice of cancelling the class. There are a few youngsters in the group, but most of the group are of retirement age, and the oldest is in her eighties. I was worried they might not fare well in the cold. Cue a chorus of disapproval. You could practically see your breath, but they were not to be dissuaded. 'It's only a bit chilly,' they said. 'We'll just have to keep moving.'

I abandoned my lesson plan and began an energetic warm-up, followed by lots of standing postures and references to *tejas* (heat or the element of fire). Never miss a chance to include a bit of philosophy! Not for the first time I was struck by how wonderful these women are. They each have something to contend with – creaky knees, blood pressure issues or painful joints – but they never miss a beat. They turn up week after week, and while there is often a bit of huffing and puffing, they just get on with it. They listen to me, but more importantly, they listen to their bodies.

Perhaps this is the wisdom that comes with age. In other classes, I have had slender young things come along to give yoga a try, but they don't come back because tight muscles don't allow their body to meet their mind's expectations. My older ladies have no such issues. They will hold on to the wall if their balance is a little off and will sit rather than kneel if that suits them better. They wear what's comfy and laugh if their belly gets in the way. They don't compete, they explore. It's always a joyful class.

These women are strong and flexible. Mentally, they are always in the moment. Once the class begins, they are totally focused (well, they look it!) and seem to be able to block out external distractions such as music from the church group that meets in the room below us. Many is the time we have lain down to relax just as they have struck up with 'A Great and Mighty Wonder'!

The American comedian Phyllis Diller said, 'You know you're getting old when your back starts going out more than you do.' Perhaps she should have tried yoga.

Suffer the little children

A few years ago, I took an extra training course to qualify in teaching yoga to children. My reasoning was that youngsters are often very receptive to new ideas and the sooner we can get them thinking about their wellbeing the better. I came away inspired to preach the yoga gospel to a new generation.

It began well enough. I worked in pre-school nurseries with tots who, naturally enough, didn't know their right from their left and in some cases their arse from their elbow. No matter, we had fun. I worked in lovely village schools where classroom assistants were on hand to help with crowd control and clothing mishaps.

I also worked in overcrowded town schools where it was clear that I was little more than a childminder while the teachers got on with their marking. I'm not blaming them, but it wasn't what I signed up for. I wasn't comfortable being left with a crowd of twenty Year 3 children who clearly believed they knew more about yoga, indeed life in general, than I did.

On one memorable occasion in this school, one poor lad piddled where he stood with no warning. I had a dilemma: should I swoop him up and take him somewhere (where?) and abandon the others or carry on and let him paddle until playtime? In the event, I went to the door and shouted for help.

Then there was this. I was thinking that the class had gone well. First time with a new group of 11 students, all yoga beginners. We'd had a chat at the start to share our expectations and together had worked through the programme gently and with good humour, or so I thought.

Then my ego got a jolt when a voice to my left said: 'When is this Godforsaken class going to finish?'

I was rather taken aback, but I wasn't annoyed because the person with this brutally honest approach was only four years old. I was a bit disappointed that he wasn't crying out for more (and I wondered where he'd heard that particular turn of phrase), but I just smiled at him and reassured him that it was nearly home time, which seemed to pacify him. I just hope that his experience with me hasn't put him off yoga for life.

When I have newcomers at any of my adult classes, I always have a word with them at the end to ask for their feedback. I want them to tell me honestly if they enjoyed it or hated it. That isn't because I would change my class to suit them, not least because if I did that I'd inevitably upset someone else; it's rather because if they found my class too strong or too slow, too lighthearted or too heavy on the philosophy, I could direct them to another teacher in the area who might suit them better.

It isn't nice when you find you've not given a student what she wants, but it's good to know the reasons why people don't come back. If I was repeatedly being told that my voice was too loud, for instance, I could do something about it. What is worse, though, is when a newbie is really enthusiastic at the end – 'I loved it! It's just what I needed. I'll definitely be back next week,' – and then I never see them again. Was it something I said? Have their circumstances changed? Have they fallen under a bus, or what? It would just be good to know.

Now I come to think about it; there was another voice of dissent in the reception class. One of the little girls was adamant that she wasn't allowed to lie on her back in case it messed up her hair.

Good grief.

Mat matters

During my training to teach yoga to children, we were instructed to work without mats. The reasoning behind this was that if we were to work in schools, there might not be enough mats to go around the whole class, and if the children couldn't have one to themselves, why should the teacher? This really took me aback. Work without a mat? Are you mad? I really need my mat! (Ah, there's the problem: a sharp lesson in non-attachment, I think!)

I did as I was told, but it felt very strange at first. Being well versed in the British Wheel of Yoga concerns about safety, I was conscious of the risk of slipping, even though we were working on carpet. When we explored Downward-facing Dog, for instance, even though we were encouraged to put our heels up against the wall for security, I couldn't stop worrying about my hands sliding away, and I was genuinely fearful that I might land on my nose. I did wonder, too, how comfortable it would be to work on a hard-wooden floor and had visions of spines rubbing on the floorboards and knees crunching.

It was more than that, though. My mat is my space. Yes, I can practise impromptu asanas on the living room carpet, but for a 'proper' session I roll out my mat. It is as though I have to get in the zone, not only mentally but also physically. When I step on to my mat, I'm stepping into my practice, and I feel

42

my mood change because my body and mind know what's coming next. It's familiar, comfortable and comforting.

I am very protective of my mat. It is common courtesy to step over someone else's belongings in class, including a mat. I don't mind if someone strays on to mine accidentally, but having to invite someone into my space isn't easy. When I go to workshops with other yogis where we work in small groups we inevitably end up sitting on each other's mats, which is OK under the circumstances (but does it make me a bad person that I take a sneaky peak to check for athlete's foot?). Sometimes we sit on our mats to eat our lunch, and I get really miffed if I have to shake off the granary breadcrumbs before I can resume for the afternoon session (and, yes, I know that reveals a less-than-generous spirit on my part).

Just to be clear, however, I feel equally uncomfortable about what I see as trespassing on someone else's territory. Working in pairs, for instance, I would always rather work on my mat and then move to my partner's when it is her turn. Nor do I like using mats in, say, a health club or gym that are used by all and sundry. Mind you, this is mostly down to practical concerns: do I really want to put my face where an unknown stranger has had his sweaty body?

Some people believe that their mat becomes charged with their energy, so perhaps it is understandable that they are uncomfortable if someone else uses it. Maybe that's why I don't like sharing. (I pondered this as I got my mat out of the washing-machine this morning, it having been necessary to clean it up after a session of yoga in a friend's garden. Have I washed away the energy and experience stored in it?)

Let's go back to the start, for a moment. Perhaps the trainer at the children's yoga session had a point, and there are good reasons to work without a mat. Certainly, the ancient yogi sages wouldn't have used them. The *Hatha Yoga Pradipika* gives clear guidance on the 'secluded yogi hut' having to be 'free of stones, fire and dampness', but in none of the translations I have seen does it also mention rolling out a mat in a favourable position. Nor can I imagine Patanjali unfurling one before settling down to his practice.

At a workshop I attended, run by the astonishing Shiva Rea we all laid out our mats in neat rows, but only minutes into the session she was beckoning us all forward to sit together – yes, on each other's mats! – and the effect was immediate and wonderful. We went from being a room of 150 strangers to a community sharing a common experience. We did return to our mats for some strenuous physical work, but then the grand finale was exploring what she described as 'the mat-less space'. We put all our bags and belongings to the edges of the room and came together for chanting, music, movement and dance. It was yoga, but unlike anything I had ever experienced before. I found it challenging on so many levels and yet liberating, too.

If yoga is truly to be a way of life, maybe we shouldn't be hidebound by having the right gear.

Sure, it's useful to be able to use the edges for alignment, and as a teacher, it is helpful to be able to guide my students by saying, 'You should be facing the short edge of your mat.' Yet if we get the urge to launch into a Salute to the Sun on the beach, we should be able just to go for it and not let the fact that we don't have a mat under our arm get in the way of the chance to practise pure, instinctive yoga.

On balance, though, I think I'll stick with my trusty mat. My scruples about hygiene, my concerns about slipping and grinding my bones into the floor and, yes, my ongoing battle with non-attachment mean that I really, truly need my mat. It's just not the same without it.

Time for a fresh start

Yoga boring? Surely not. That's a word only applied to monotonous routines in the gym or time spent pounding away on a treadmill. Maybe so, but we could all benefit from shaking up our practice once in a while. Try these suggestions to add a bit of freshness.

Your personal practice is complemented by regular class attendance, but are you making the most of it? Do you always roll out your mat in the same spot in the back left-hand corner of the room? Be bold: move to the front. Change your perspective and literally look at things from a different angle. Don't be shy about asking your teacher questions: why are we doing this? What are the benefits? What else can I work on at home alongside this?

Attend a different class for a change. There are so many ways of teaching even the familiar postures, such as Triangle, that working with asana you think you know well can be an eye-opener when someone new talks you into it. A different teacher will use different patter, so you might have to concentrate a bit more than usual, which is no bad thing. Even better, try a new style. For instance, if you are a dyed-in-the-wool hatha student, join an ashtanga class every once in a while.

If you usually go to a full-on, dedicated yoga class, try it in a gym; or for a really different approach, how about a turn on an interactive electronic fitness program? After many years of practising yoga the traditional way, my ego took a bit of a hit when my Wii Fit Plus told me my Downward-facing Dog was only of beginner standard! It made me think, though, about weight distribution and that there might be another way to approach this posture. Is it best to focus on core strength to keep me steady, or on taking my body weight back into my legs or working to improve my arm strength? Or, as is so often the case, is the answer: 'It depends'?

Not all towns have lots of yoga teachers to choose from, so you might have to go further afield and sign up for a one-day workshop or even a weekend course in order to work with someone new. We can't all spend a year in an ashram, but there's no doubt that even a few hours immersed in yoga with a bunch of likeminded fellows can be truly refreshing and can rekindle your enthusiasm for the familiar, as well as opening your heart and mind to new possibilities.

Splash out on a one-to-one session. A fresh pair of objective eyes can help you discover ways to enhance your personal practice by assessing your range of movement and your physical strengths and weaknesses. We can all be tempted to work on what we like rather than what we need, but sometimes being told by an outsider that you would benefit from working on, say, a Boat balance (my least favourite asana of them all!) can give you the impetus you need, particularly if you book a follow-up session.

Liven up your home practice by working with postures you've never done before. Subscribe to an online yoga channel. Buy or borrow a yoga book with good illustrations and let it fall open at a random page. Resolve to master that posture, and that means preparatory and follow-up work, too. Of course, if it lands on Savasana, that lovely lying down pose we adopt at the end for relaxation, have another go!

Writes the names of as many postures as you can think of on separate pieces of paper. Shuffle them well, turn them face down and pick three. Find a way to move through them in a sequence.

If you normally work with separate asanas, try a few flows. Put 'yoga vinyasa' in your internet search engine and see what pops up to inspire you.

Choose a posture you're really comfortable with and explore new ways of working with it. Do you do a Cat stretch every day? Vary it by doing it standing up and observe how this changes the physical and energetic effects. Or do four Salutes to the Sun but with a different focus each time: earth (grounding); air (keep it light); water (smooth and flowing); and fire (speed it up to generate heat).

Does 'balance' to you mean standing on one leg? Then how about working on an arm balance, such as Crow?

A complete yoga practice means flexibility and strength, so don't forget to include a challenging plank, as well as tying yourself in knots in Lotus.

How do you feel about props? If you're one of those who feels that using a block for support is cheating, think again. Judicious use of props can help to take the fear out of a balance or can allow you to surrender more deeply because the belt, bolster or whatever takes care of one element and leaves you free to explore another. Supporting the weight of your leg with a strap in a pose such as Standing Big Toe Balance could enable you to focus on working on your hamstrings. Conversely, if you never set foot in a class without a complete yoga toolkit, perhaps you should consider that rather than using props, you are actually leaning on crutches.

The term 'prop' can be extended to mean another person. Not everyone is comfortable with the level of intimacy involved in partner work, but it can be a useful way to add another dimension.

Take it outside. OK, perhaps not in the midst of a British winter; but when the weather starts to warm up, get in touch with nature by taking your mat into the garden. Even when it's a bit fresh, though, some pranayama on a windy hillside can be very invigorating.

Conventionally, asanas are followed by pranayama and then meditation, but is this the only way? If you know you've got a challenging day ahead, you might want to meditate before work to put yourself in the right frame of mind and then do some energetic physical stuff to revitalise you when you get home. Drop some pranayama into your day as and when it's needed, even if that simply means *bastrika* (Bellows Breath) when the heating breaks down, and you've got all the bases covered.

Don't forget the other side of yoga. Keep up your reading; explore the philosophy of the

Upanishads; consider leading a life in accordance with the *yamas* and *niyamas*, the yoga philosophical guidelines on how to treat ourselves, other people and the wider world.

Familiarity breeds, if not contempt, at least a lack of progress, so mix things up a bit and there will never be a dull moment.

The great outdoors

Can there be a better way to enjoy your yoga than to take your practice outside? Whether you pick a shady spot in your garden or wander through a park, a patch of woodland, on a beach or up in the mountains, here are some simple ways in which you can get back to nature and connect with the earth's energies.

We all spend too much time indoors and in our cars, and bad habits creep into our breathing if we let them. So, start your outdoor session with some wonderful, deep breaths. Work with the yoga three-part breath and feel the air pushing out your abdomen, filling your lungs and expanding your ribcage to the front, sides and back, and lifting your collar bones. Hold the breath as long as is comfortable, and then release it along the same pathway, holding your breath out. Encourage your out-breath to be longer than your in-breath, and you will feel your whole body start to relax: and once that happens, your mind won't be far behind it.

Focus on breathing properly as you walk along, or when you are sitting comfortably on a park bench or the grass out in the countryside. Work with other breathing practices and pranayama: alternate nostril breathing or *ujjayi,* perhaps. Breathe in as deeply as you can to take in a good lungful of clean air, and when you breathe out, empty the bottom pockets of your lungs and get rid of all the staleness that has accumulated there. Don't force your breath, however, because your lungs are delicate and must be treated with respect. Even if it's raining, you can pull on your wellies, get out there and simply breathe.

Kick off your shoes and take a slow, mindful walk. Enjoy the texture of the ground against your skin, the tickle of the grass or the sand as it works its way between your toes, or notice how the earth and rocks are hot beneath your bare feet. Be aware of the tiny movements in the muscles and joints in your feet and toes, and notice how this relates to work going on elsewhere in your body. What can you feel? How slowly can you walk without starting to wobble? Now, lift your head: you know where your feet are, you don't have to watch them. Breathe, slowly and deeply and enjoy the sensations.

Some postures cry out to be done outside, particularly the standing asanas that are inherently grounding. Put aside your mat and get your feet dirty.

Start with Tadasana, and spread your feet as you connect with the earth and come to a point of stillness. Now follow your instincts and without thinking about it too much, ease yourself into another posture. Triangle follows on nicely and gives you the chance to keep your feet grounded while taking your shoulders back to open your chest and your heart to the elements. Meanwhile, your upper hand reaches skywards.

How about working with Warrior I and Warrior II? Again, everything below your waist is centred and grounded, but above your waist is light and focused upwards. Move from one posture to the other in a gentle flow to keep your energy moving. If you like sequences, work with any version of Salute to the Sun, or go out in the evening and Salute to the Moon.

Doing yoga outside challenges your perceptions. You will have to work harder to balance on a rough surface than you do inside. Surely the balance that must be done outside is Tree: but if the wind blows, do you bend or break? You may find different muscles kicking in as you work to retain your pose.

Eagle, too, is a great one if you are trying to emulate nature. Get your hands down on the ground and work in Firefly arm balance – but make sure that you will have a soft landing, just in case. In fact, pick any of the animal postures: Cat, Dog, Dolphin, Cobra, Locust, the list goes on. Work with their characteristics in mind to bring in a new element, such as the sinewy strength of the Lizard or the grace of the Peacock. Let your imagination take over.

Conclude your practice with a meditation. Mother Nature is generous in her provision of objects for focus. Train your gaze on the gorgeous formation of a rosebud, the array of colours in the leaves, the twist of a seashell, the pattern in a rock or the glory of a setting sun. Alternatively, listen to the sounds around you. Are there people about? Distant traffic? Music playing? Can you focus beyond these noises and pick up the sounds of nature, such as birdsong, flowing water or insects buzzing? What about smells, such as blossom or the sea? Or simply sit content in your natural surroundings and enjoy your own breath, cool as it flows in and warm as it flows out, smoothly and peacefully. Wrap something around your shoulders to ward off a chilly breeze, or sit in the shade if the sun is hot and protect yourself from burning.

We are so cocooned in our everyday life that sometimes we forget how beautiful our world is. Take the plunge, open your door, lift your gaze, allowing the sun to shine on it and nature will heal your soul.

Resolving not to resolve

One of the many advantages of being self-employed and working from home is that I'm freed from the tyranny of the alarm clock. I don't teach every morning, nor am I responsible for rousing anyone else, so I simply sleep until I wake. Surprisingly, this doesn't mean I'm still in my pit at lunchtime, but I'm able to open my eyes and ease gently into the day.

On the rare occasions when I do need to be somewhere early on, the previous night as I go to bed I bang my head on the pillow the appropriate number of times. If, say, I need to be in the shower by 6.15, the night before I simply bang my head six times before I settle down to sleep. I don't know how this works, but it does, although I will also set my clock, just in case. I'm not daft.

I like the feeling that I've woken up naturally. It's a pity I can't live in harmony with nature in other aspects of my life. Remember those New Year resolutions you made on 1st January? How did they pan out for you? Did you lose that weight? Have you been practising your yoga every day before work? Still going to that conversational Italian evening class, you enrolled for? Thought so.

The trouble with the New Year is that it falls in the middle of winter. Who wants to eat salad when there are pies to be made, and the markets groan under the weight of root vegetables just crying out to be made into stews? And where there is stew, there must surely be dumplings.

I have decided that a new year can start at any time. How about designating spring as the best time to start a new regime? Make March the new January. As nature begins to blossom and there is that unmistakeable hint of freshness in the year, it's easier to feel invigorated. I'm much more likely to strap on my walking boots if the sun is out than when it's cold and miserable. I might even want to spring-clean my house, to open the windows wide and let in some light and air. I often get a surge of energy in September. Perhaps it's harking back to the academic year, or maybe it's because I was an autumn baby, but this is when I want to clear the decks and sharpen my pencils.

I don't care what the calendar says, while it's still winter there's always time for one more fully laden hot chocolate. Can someone pass me the marshmallows, please?

Instinct vs intellect: what rules you?

In yoga, we know that we should never push ourselves into anything that is uncomfortable and that we should work within our own limits. But what sets those limits: instinct or intellect?

When I was pregnant with Number Two Son, I craved cheese spread, straight from the jar. I told myself that it was fine to pig out because my body must want the calcium. Was I following my instincts and seeking out the nutrients I needed, or was I trying to rationalise my greed and using my condition as an excuse to overeat something that I would normally eschew as a nasty processed food?

The question of instinct versus intellect can vex yoga students and teachers of all levels. At what point, does or should one take over from the other; and how easy is it to tell which is which anyway?

When you are working on a difficult pose, is it self-knowledge or fear that holds you back from taking one more deep breath and going for that extra twist or stretch? You might think you are listening to your instincts and that you have gone as far as is safe, but as Henry Ford and others have said: 'Whether you think you can or think that you can't, you are right.' Too much thinking can get in the way of the flow. Could it be that with a little encouragement you could go further than you ever have before?

57

Part of yoga is to explore what your body can do and to deepen your experience by experimenting with postures, tweaking a foot position here or extending a breathing practice there. Sometimes you need to feel your way to challenge yourself.

In his *Yoga Sutras*, Patanjali is clear about the role that the mind plays in physical practice and sets out the *klesha* (obstacles) to controlling the mind and how to overcome them. As yogis, we need to be in charge of our mind, so that we can put fear and preconceptions aside and let our abilities flourish.

When it comes to exploring a posture, it is a fine line between working with what is your maximum today and going just a bit too far. 'Just see what your body will do,' your teacher advises, but that's easier said than done. We can become bound by what we think we can achieve, rather than what we are actually capable of.

If you tell yourself you cannot do a full headstand, for instance, you are setting yourself up to fail. You get halfway into the posture; then your mind says: 'That's it, that's as far as I can go,' and you bring your body down. You don't want to fall, so you hold back, but is this an instinctive fear or has reason taken over? Has your mind already thought through what would happen if you were to tumble flat on your back? Fear of falling is one of only two fears we are born with (the other is loud noises), but perhaps your intellect has stopped you achieving your goal.

Yet suppressing your instincts can work against you in other ways, too, making you go too far, rather than not far enough. We all know that yoga is not competitive, but if you are in a class and have been told to hold Plough 'only as long as feels comfortable', it can be really tempting to grit your teeth and carry on longer than you truly want to. Your instinct may be screaming at you to stop: 'Tonight I am tired and I've had enough.' Meanwhile, your intellect – ambition, pride, whatever you like to call it – is saying: 'I must keep going. I don't want to be the first to stop. I should be able to hold this for longer.' So you do, and suffer the consequences the next day.

If you have an injury, you will inevitably need to modify your practice to take account of temporary physical limitations, but when do you allow yourself to increase the work to your former level? If you know you have a weakness somewhere, do you only do movements that avoid working that part, or do seek out postures that will build strength there? If you've had a sprained wrist, does that mean that you will never do Cat again? It's a fine line between being sensible and being overcautious. What are you going to listen to: 'I'm not supposed to do this' or 'I'd like to see if I can'?

Often, it is a mental rather than a physical impediment that stops us progressing. For years, I told myself that I didn't have the strength in my arms to do the Wheel. Then I worked with a group of people where it was assumed that we could all do this posture to some degree or other. It was as though being given permission to work within my own limits – to *not* do the posture – took the pressure off. We worked gradually: warm-ups for wrists, arms and shoulders, feet and legs; a range of back arches to stretch and open our bodies; using props and supports; working in pairs, and finding ways to modify when and how we needed to. When it came, the transition into the final posture seemed natural. I had been given the techniques and the confidence to lift myself off the ground and just go for it.

Of course, if you've been told by a medical professional that something could exacerbate a condition or cause irreparable harm, you must acknowledge that advice. If the limitations are self-imposed, however, perhaps it's time to start investigating what you can do, rather than what you can't. Just surrender to the moment.

Ultimately, it's your body and your practice, so don't be afraid to push yourself a little bit. Take responsibility and trust your instincts. You will be amazed at what you achieve.

Yoga is not a competition

Sometimes I spot a student wearing 'the look'. She might be holding a posture beautifully, but I can see on her face the signs that all is not well. At this point, I remind the class: 'Patanjali says *"Sthira sukham asanam."* Asana is a steady, comfortable posture.' Then I go and stand by said student and say again, 'Yoga isn't competitive. Come out of the posture whenever you're ready.'

Some people just won't be told. They think they look tranquil, but I can see the tension creeping up their body, their teeth are clenched and there is a hint of panic in their eyes. They simply won't allow themselves to release until everyone else has finished.

You can't teach people what they're not ready to learn. For some, the idea of listening to their body and stopping when they've had enough, even if others have not, is a hard one. Nor is this limited to ordinary classes; I'm afraid I've also seen this phenomenon at teacher training sessions, where we really should know better.

Then there are those who like to challenge themselves beyond the point that is beneficial or even safe. These are often the super fit, the strong and the flexible who can normally do everything asked of them. An off day isn't an option. OK, so maybe they've twisted their ankle while out running: so what? Do you think that's going to stop them holding Warrior II until they shake?

I regularly remind my students that if I ask them to do something and it doesn't feel right, even if they can usually do it, then they should work gently and not push themselves too hard. But that man, for example, who has found out his blood pressure is, unusually for him, elevated might not like to hear that he should keep his arms down.

There is no denying the joy of manoeuvring yourself into an asana you thought was beyond you, but it's a fine line between exploring what your body is capable of and going too far. I can encourage safe practice and highlight the need for caution, but ultimately the individual has responsibility for his or her own wellbeing.

If I have a particularly stubborn student in the class who won't heed my safety guidelines, I will say, 'OK, folks, you all heard me warn her!' I try to keep it lighthearted, but really what I'm saying is: 'Please don't sue me if you fall over!'

Surrender to yoga

Anyone who has ever been skiing will know there are no half measures when it comes to jumping on to a button lift. You just have to go for it, because if you hesitate you will miss your chance. The longer you prevaricate, the more anxious you become and the harder it gets to take that leap of faith and trust that that tiny circle of plastic will transport you safely to the top of the run.

There are lots of things that are easier if you just launch yourself in with total commitment. There is no gradual entry into a bungee jump, for instance, and it's always better to dive straight into a cold swimming pool than to sit with your legs dangling over the side and lower yourself in, gasping as the chill spreads up your body.

Now, I'm not suggesting for a moment that you should throw caution to the wind and leap into your asanas without a second thought; but I am suggesting that sometimes you should take courage, let go and see what happens. I encourage my students to go as far they can in a posture and then stop, observe how they feel, and then perhaps go a bit deeper (or perhaps not: no pressure!).

Think about balance. As beginners, we may tell ourselves that we can't stand on one leg in Warrior III, so we cling to the back of a chair for support. But what if we breathe deeply, relax and let go, literally and figuratively? What if we surrender to the moment and trust that our body and mind will do what we ask of them? What's the worst that could happen? A bit of a wobble and the necessity to bring a foot to the floor or put out a hand to steady ourselves; but what if it turned out that we could actually maintain a wonderful, steady posture?

How about something more challenging, such as the Crow? Fear of landing on my nose held me back for a long time. I was, quite simply, too insecure to tip my hips high enough and shift my centre of gravity forwards. But one day, working with a different teacher and surrounded by a nest of cushions and a supportive atmosphere, I found that if I just lifted my feet and committed I could do it.

As is so often the case with any aspect of yoga, one of the best aids to surrender is breathing. Do you know that wonderful sigh you give out when you sit down after a hard day on your feet and sink into a welcoming armchair? Use your out-breath properly, and you can get the same feeling in your postures.

Think about this. You're standing in a modification of Warrior I, up on the ball of your back foot, legs taking the strain, with your arms alongside your ears and your back arched into a gentle bend. Hard work, yes?

Now surrender. Stop thinking about it, just do it. With every out-breath, allow your body to settle down, and instead of gritting your teeth to hold the posture rigidly, allow a little movement and some minor but constant adjustments so that you can stay there for longer. Unclench those teeth and commit to the posture. You're where you're meant to be, and you are safe.

In a military sense, to surrender means to stop resisting an opponent and submit to his authority, but it can also mean abandoning oneself completely to a powerful emotion or influence. Consider what it is that is holding you back. Why is it sometimes so difficult to relinquish control and simply be? Is it fear? Lack of knowledge? Self-criticism? Or is it ego? If you are so bothered by other people, your mind will turn your practice into a competition, which results in you limiting your own experience. Are you too attached to your practice and so unable to step outside and simply observe? Once you know why you put on the brakes, you can start to do something about it.

There is also a deeper, more philosophical aspect to surrender. The last of Patanjali's *niyamas* discusses *Isvara Pranidhanani*: by total surrender to God, *samadhi* is attained.

Depending on your spiritual perspective, this might be an uncomfortable concept. Sri Swami Satchidananda's commentary defines it as a life of dedication, of offering everything to the Lord or, crucially, to humanity, which perhaps makes it more accessible. Patanjali seems to be saying that we can achieve anything we give ourselves and our actions to the greater good. It ties in with that yoga notion of *vairagyam* or non-attachment. If we do things for their own sake rather than our own benefit, it is possible to remain separate and tranquil. From here the path to meditation becomes clearer, and perhaps even *samadhi* is achievable.

In the twentieth-first century, we are used to being in control of our own destiny, and the idea of relinquishing that control to an unknown, unseen being can be unnerving or even frightening. We want immediate, tangible results and instant gratification, and not some nebulous consequence of our actions. Yet, the concept of surrender is fundamental to all religions and a goal of all spiritual paths.

In *The Heart of Yoga*, Desikachar says: 'We must teach a person what he or she can accept at the time, not what we think would finally be best for them.' Maybe you're not ready to surrender to your god; I know I find this a tricky idea to connect with. For now, I'm content to work on letting go with a kind of 'let's see what happens' attitude.

I might not be paving my way to the kingdom of heaven, *samadhi*, nirvana or wherever, but I might just be able to take my yoga practice to another level.

Any way the wind blows

My class had been lying in a beautiful semi-supine position, breathing gently just to be there, tuning in and scanning their bodies to see how they were feeling that day in body and mind. All was calm.

In preparation for what was to come, I suggested they bring their knees to their chest and hug them in close, perhaps with a little circling and gentle rocking. Suddenly the serenity was disturbed by a thunderous anal raspberry. Not for nothing is this position called *apanasana*, the wind-reliever.

There was a pause before she who dealt it said, 'Sorry, girls. Just getting the energy moving!' Thus, the tension was broken, and we were given permission to laugh.

Something else that cannot be controlled, no matter how we try, is when and where we drop off to sleep. On one occasion, I suggested to a habitual snoozer that she might try to relax on a chair, rather than lying down. I hoped it would help her to stay awake.

I guided the class to that point where I stop talking and they take themselves to a place of stillness. With every out-breath, my chair-bound student leaned a little bit further to the left. I tiptoed over to her, not sure whether to wake her up or just get ready to catch her. Just when she seemed to have reached tipping point, she righted herself and started to lean the other way. She continued to move precariously from one extreme to the other, never quite toppling and never opening her eyes. At the end of the session, she declared herself to be satisfactorily refreshed.

It's amazing what a body can do when it's uninhibited; so, is it possible that we put up obstacles in our yoga practice that our body would overcome if left to its own devices? If you know you have creaky knees, for instance, do you shy away from postures that challenge them because you think you won't be able to do them? Do you tell yourself you can't stand on one leg and go straight to the wall for support whenever anyone says 'balance'?

Stop thinking about it and simply do it. Trust your body. It might just come up trumps.

Someone's sitting there, mate

Does it really matter where you are in the room? I went to stay with some friends recently, and they invited me to join them for Sunday morning worship. On the way, they stopped to pick up another friend, Diane, just as they do every week. It struck me as rather odd, therefore, that once inside the church Diane chose to sit across the aisle, not only away from us but also completely on her own. Worried that my presence might be upsetting her in some way, I asked my friend if this was the case.

'Oh no, that's just where Diane always sits,' she replied. 'That's her seat.'

When newcomers attend my classes I always invite them to roll out their mats anywhere they like and then I introduce them to their neighbours. My aim is to make them as comfortable as possible in new surroundings. Sometimes, though, it causes consternation when one of my students turns up to find 'her' place taken by a stranger. Even odder, if one of my regulars is away, her space tends to be left empty, unless I specifically suggest that everyone spreads out to take advantage of the room.

One of my teaching rooms was out of action for a few weeks, instead of being in a large school hall we had to hold sessions in a classroom. This threw us into confusion. I wasn't able to stand where I would normally to check off the register and take the money. The clock was in the wrong place and instead of lying in gently curving rows, my students had to be more regimented to squeeze into a much smaller space than usual, and I had to work harder to remember who was where.

The sounds around us were different, and because we had a wall of windows on the left instead of ceiling-height windows behind us, the light was different, too. We had to move cautiously to avoid clattering into unaccustomed furniture or connecting with people who are lying in unexpected places. Even the difference between working on a wooden floor and carpet was noticed.

Sometimes there are good reasons to work in the same spot every week: perhaps to have easy access to a chair or to be sure of hearing what's going on. How much of this is simply habit, and if where we put our mat is a habit, how much of the class is done on automatic pilot?

Perhaps I need to shake things up a bit and teach from a different corner each week – or maybe that would just confuse me too much.

Incy Wincy posture

Surveying my students, I was pleased by their focus and steadiness, as they held a secure Urdhva Hastasana, a strong standing posture in which the arms are held along in upward salutation. From some came the gentle purr of *ujjayi* (Victory Breath). All was well.

My eyes scanned the rows of ladies, taking in the tranquillity of the scene, but then I did a double take as my eyes were drawn back to Elsie in the middle of the room. She had begun to lean at an interesting angle, and her expression was changing from serene to restless. I was concerned that she might be about to topple over, but I caught her eye and, with the gentlest of head movements, she summoned me over.

'Spider,' she whispered. 'There's a massive spider crawling over Doris's mat.' Sure enough, there was, and it was the size of a dinner plate. Well, OK, not a dinner plate exactly, but it was certainly 10cm across its diameter. I'm not frightened of spiders, but even so, I was taken aback.

With as much nonchalance as I could muster, I sidled up to Doris and quietly asked her if she was feeling steady and comfortable.

'Yes, thank you,' she whispered back.

'Wonderful. And how do you feel about spiders?'

'They're all right in their place. Why?' At which point she looked down.

I think it's fair to say that she came out of the posture much quicker than she had gone into it, but to her credit she didn't scream. Nevertheless, the rest of the group realised something was amiss, lowered their arms and opened their eyes.

The spider must have been affected by stage fright, because instead of scuttling away it simply sat there looking at us. Various suggestions were made as to what its fate might be. In the spirit of *ahimsa* (non-violence), I opted not to whack it with a yoga block and instead scooped it up in a cup and transported it downstairs, where I released it back into the wild.

Back in the room, the mood was broken, and a conversation had arisen about the nature of phobias and how irrational they can be. I've been known to be held prisoner downstairs at home, because of a moth standing guard on the landing light.

In celebration of the wild thing that had visited us, we took ourselves into various versions of Camatkarasana, the posture of that name. Then, stretching a point perhaps, we considered the Wheel, which many of us knew better from our playground days as the Crab. On the spur of the moment, this was the nearest we could come to a Spider posture.

Look at me, look at me!

You're easing yourself into a wide-legged forward bend when suddenly you catch the eye of the woman working on the mat next to you. What goes through your mind?

Oh no, she's looking at me. I'd better try harder, even though I'm stretched to my maximum.

Oh no, she's looking at me. Bet she thinks I'm rubbish/fat/showing off.

Oh great, she's looking at me. After all, I'm really good at this posture.

And what is she thinking?

Wow, she's really good at this posture. What an inspiration!

Oh good, she's rubbish/fat/showing off. I'm much better/thinner/more focused than she is.

Oh no, she's really good at this posture. I'll never be as good as her.

Whatever your response, it's your ego that is rearing its ugly head. In reality, of course, the chances are that most people are too busy grappling with their own asana to worry about what you are doing. (Ego again: why should they be interested in you?)

Look in the dictionary, and you will find ego defined as 'I or self; that which is conscious and thinks; an image of oneself; self-confidence.' Nothing wrong with ego, then, but in the west we generally jump straight to the definition not of ego, but of egotistic: 'self-centred; selfish; having an inflated sense of one's own importance.' Suddenly a word that is emotionally neutral becomes an indication of something bad.

Being egotistic can make us over-competitive and disgruntled with our lot. 'I must be the best' is not as good a mantra as 'I must do my best.' Nevertheless, having a strong ego is important, if it means that we know who we are and where our strengths and weaknesses lie. In many works of life, competition is healthy. You're probably not going to get that promotion, for instance, if you don't put yourself forwards. You need to have sufficient inner strength and confidence to know that you could do the job well.

This is not what ego means in a yoga class. One of the things that makes it so different from other forms of activity is that it goes beyond the physical. Yes, we all want to do the postures to the best of our ability, but the key phrase is 'best of our ability', that is to say, not better than the person working on the mat next to us. We should not be competing to hold the postures for longer, lift our legs higher, twist our spines further or earn the most acknowledgement from the teacher. This attitude perpetuates the idea that our bodies are separate from our selves.

We need to work to connect with our inner self, to look inwards at who we really are, not what we do or to define ourselves by our relationships with others as partner, parent, team member, colleague or friend.

The Sanskrit word for ego meant in the sense of self or 'I am-ness' is *ahamkara*. It is the part of your consciousness that is self-aware and deals with wants and desires. One way to begin to understand *ahamkara* is through the practice of non-attachment. This means not clinging to possessions or emotions that tie you to the outside world and distract you. (This is not the same as detachment, which I interpret as a complete rejection of wants and needs, and that I always think sounds rather callous.)

It's not called yoga practice for nothing. The aim isn't to work your way through a list of asanas and tick them off as you do them. You must practise, explore, modify, develop, adapt. One day you can't hold a plank posture for more than a few seconds; the next day you manage a bit longer; but on day three, you are back where you started.

Instead of letting your ego chastise you for getting 'worse', say to yourself, 'That's interesting. What is different about me today? Am I tired? Distracted? Unhappy? Have I eaten something that has affected me?' This is what being non-attached means: remaining uncritical, but observant, enquiring and connected with what's really going on inside you.

It isn't you in the pure sense that is any different. It is just that your body, the external representation of you that people see, is responding to stimuli in a way today that it didn't do yesterday and probably won't do tomorrow. Work to develop feelings of non-attachment so that you can look at your body objectively and non-judgementally.

In his *Yoga Sutras*, Patanjali talks about the five obstacles to 'distinguished contemplation': ignorance, egoism, attachment, hatred and clinging to bodily life. Note the order. As Swami Satchidananda says in commentary on the *Sutras*, egoism is the result of ignorance of the self. We need to get to know our self and our true nature, or, to put it simply, to understand what makes us tick.

The first of Patanjali's eight limbs or *yamas* includes *ahimsa*, that is, non-violence or causing no harm. This must be applied to ourselves, as well as to others. If our ego encourages us to go just a bit further in a seated wide-legged forward bend until that gentle stretching feeling in the satorius muscles changes into a searing pain, that's bad. So what if the super-flexible woman on the front row can place her chest on the floor? You are not her, and she isn't you.

That's not to say that we shouldn't try to improve our practice, to become more diligent and persevere when we come up against a problem or an asana that we find challenging. But even here, the ego can throw up obstacles. Consider the use of props. Help or hindrance? A sign of self-awareness or weakness?

The teacher says, 'Let's work with a Tree balance.' You can tell as soon as you lift your foot off the floor that this is going to be a challenge. Do you take yourself to a wall for support, or do you stand doggedly on your mat in the middle of the room wavering around all over the place? Do you keep your big toe in contact with the floor or do you (like the woman in front of you!), lift your foot on to your lower leg, or even on to your inner thigh and present an image not of a tree – strong, centre, grounded – but more like something that has just felt the wrath of a lumberjack's axe, toes curled up for dear life, core muscle strength forgotten as you struggle to remain upright, arms flailing and teeth gritted in determination? You don't want to admit to yourself or anyone else in the room that today you just aren't in the balancing mood. Where is *ahimsa* now?

Yoga is a personal practice, even when done in public. I repeat: it is not a competition. Wouldn't it be better to accept that today you need support or you need to modify the posture?

As a teacher, I often instruct my students to relax in a posture, something I also try to take into my own practice. You can't do this if your ego won't accept that you've gone as far as you can today because you will be straining to push just that little bit further. Yet, once you surrender to the relaxation and allow your body to explore and settle of its own accord, you will find that you are released from the physical effort of holding your body in position. Then your connection with your breathing and the deeper effects on your body on a pranic (energetic) level are able to come to the fore.

Try not to see ego as a bad thing associated with overconfidence and arrogance. It is perhaps a peculiarly British trait always to favour the underdog and judge anyone who is confident in their abilities as cocky and having an inflated view of their own importance. However, if we can get over this and connect with our true self, if we can work with what we have and where we are today, if, in other words, we can strengthen our ego, rather than trying to subdue it, then we can extend our yoga practice beyond the purely physical.

Nobody likes a show-off

Let's be honest; we all like to show off from time to time, whether it's beaming proudly as you bring a fabulous pie out of the oven to an *Ooh!* of admiration or singing out on karaoke night, but you would think that the one place you could expect modesty and self-restraint would be in a yoga class.

I must hold up my hands and say that sometimes when I'm demonstrating a posture, the thought comes into my head that my students might think I'm rather good at it. I know, I know. There shouldn't be room in my mind or heart for such egotism, but if you've stuck with me this far I think you'll realise that I don't always get it right; and in my defence, I don't start by saying: 'Watch what I can do!'

I mention this because I've had a couple of strange experiences on yoga study days. On one occasion, I went to a teacher-training session on integrating philosophy into a general class. I was expecting some physical practice, but knew the day was going to be largely theory. Therefore, as I arrived, I was rather surprised to see one woman turned upside-down in the middle of the room with each shoulder perched precariously on a different chair and her head dangling towards the floor between them. I could only wonder why.

More recently, another training day saw a group of us grappling with the intricacies of the Sage's Pose, that deep forward bend that involves one straight leg, one bent and the hands clasped behind the back. We talked all round it and then experimented with modifications and the use of props. In the discussion session after the practical work, one of our number raised her hand and said she wasn't sure she was feeling what she should and could we take a look at her.

I wasn't the only one whose jaw dropped as she eased herself effortlessly into the posture. Now, perhaps I'm being uncharitable, and she might genuinely have had issues, but all I heard was: 'Look at me! Look at me!'

It's all a matter of taste

I was invited to help judge a writing competition. This was a mixed blessing. On the plus side, I got to read lots of lovely stories; on the minus side, I had to pick 'the best'.

What gives me the right to judge the work of others? Well, in my other work life away from my yoga teaching, I've written and had published books, stories, articles and various other pieces of copy, and have edited hundreds over the years, but that doesn't make me better than the contestants. It does, though, suggest that I know what to look for.

Taste comes into it, of course. There were stories I just didn't like, not because they weren't well written, but because they weren't my kind of thing. However, the competition wasn't to find the one I liked best, so I had to rein in my objectivity and become more subjective.

'What's this got to do with yoga?', I hear you cry. Well, it's made me think about my own practice. Do I work with asana that meet my needs or do I pick my favourites? When I'm teaching, too, do my plans include postures for my students or for me? I must confess that there are some things I never include because, quite simply, I don't like them.

Take the wondrous posture Heron in which one leg is folded away and the other, straight leg, is lifted straight up in front of the face. Sometimes my toes fly upwards with grace and elegance, but on other days my hamstrings say, 'You want me to do what? I don't think so!' It's a work in progress for me, so I don't teach it very often. The thought of getting stuck in an ungainly position in front of my class is not appealing.

Of course, my reluctance might also be because I'm unwilling to be judged by my students. I want them to be able to trust me, and I worry that the unedifying sight of my flailing limbs might cause them to judge my ability to teach based on how long I can hold this posture. Maybe, once they'd stopped laughing, it would have the opposite effect and the fact that it's OK for their teacher to lose her poise, literally, might boost their own confidence and give them a greater willingness to try and, if necessary, have another go.

We probably all know people who only listen to one sort of music or read books from one genre. That can't be right, can it? Think of all the stuff they're missing. So, next time I catch myself thinking 'I don't like this posture', I'm going to change my mind set and give it a go.

Everybody chant, now!

Most people join a yoga class because they want to learn the postures. At the same time, they may have a vague idea that it also involves sitting around cross-legged, eyes closed, intoning 'Om'. So, what is chanting all about?

Chanting is not singing. Rather, it is the diligent, tonal repetition of a single sound, word or phrase called a mantra. Why do we do it in yoga? The short answer is: because it feels good!

Mantras are a way of helping you become aware of what's going on in your head and your inner self. They can encourage you to change bad habits for good, to turn your senses inwards, to deepen your spiritual experience and to look at the world another way; and they can be used as an act of devotion or as a tool for meditation, or to reap physical benefits derived from the vibration. Each person's experience is likely to be different.

Let's go back a bit. All matter is energy. If you had a powerful enough microscope, you could close in on, say, a flower and see that the particles it comprises are constantly moving. Different materials vibrate at different frequencies. The Sanskrit alphabet is made up of 50 letters and mantra is constructed from a combination of sounds derived from these letters. The sounds/vibrations of the mantra relate to the sounds/vibrations of the universe.

There are many different styles of mantra. Perhaps the simplest and best known is the one already mentioned: Om. This is the original and most powerful mantra and is sometimes referred to as the sound of the universal consciousness.

There are simple called *bija* (seed) mantra, which are derived directly from the 50 primeval sounds. These are words such as *Ham*, *Yam*, *Ram*, *Vam* and *Lam*, which correspond to the elements ether, air, fire, water and earth, respectively, and are imbued with properties associated with their particular vibration.

Some are associated with a particular deity. For example, *Om Gam Ganapataye Namaha* is linked to the Hindu god Ganesha, the remover of obstacles and bestower of success. Working with a mantra aimed at a god doesn't mean that you are worshipping that figure. Rather it is a way of accessing the energies or qualities associated with him. Hence, chanting with Ganesha in mind might enable you to find a way to overcome your problems, but it's not a magical incantation.

Others are more abstract – for example, *Soham*, meaning, I am that I am. These give the mind focus without affiliation to anything external. Alternatively, a mantra can be an ordinary word that resonates with the individual, such as love or harmony.

Mantras can be sacred or secular. They can be charged with energy derived from the sounds' innate vibration and can empower body and mind. The question is: do you have to understand the words to reap the benefit?

Consider how you feel when you hear Motorhead's 'Ace of Spades'. Whether you love it or hate it, it evokes an emotional and possibly physical response. Compare that to Vaughan Williams' 'The Lark Ascending'. These differing responses are aroused whether or not you know the lyrics or understand the composer's intentions. You are responding to the vibration as much as the actual sound, but it is the music rather than the words with which a connection is made. If you were to sing 'Happy Birthday to You' to the tune of the 'Funeral March', which emotion would win out: joy or sorrow? (Try it.)

Mantra isn't music. The vibration with which the connection is made is generated by the pronunciation of the words, and the words of a mantra have been chosen with care. Its effects are the result of your connection with the energy they generate. For some people, that will be enough. Others will get more out of it if they know what it is they are saying. Perhaps the crux is your intention. (The test would be to work with a mantra and discover for yourself what effect it has, without being told how it 'ought' to make you feel.)

Give it a go. Open your mind and see how you feel. Join in or just listen, but be respectful. Take from it what you need and, for now, set aside anything you don't connect with.

Music to your ears?

Music can be a mixed blessing. Walking into a quiet room full of people can be a daunting experience whatever the occasion. How would you feel at your first yoga class if everyone was settling themselves down in silence? It's amazing how loud a bag zip can sound when you are trying not to draw attention to yourself; and if you do speak, everyone can hear what you are saying. Suppose you want a quiet word with the teacher about, ahem, a 'personal issue'. Wouldn't a discreet backdrop of music be quite a comfort?

The trouble with music is that it is a very subjective thing. I love loud rock music, but wouldn't play it to my yoga students, at least, not without a very good reason; but something gentle and unobtrusive can be quite pleasant and actually encourage a hubbub of conversation. There is a place for music at the start of a class to set the mood, and again at the end as students leave if only to keep the yoga atmosphere going as long as possible. You don't want to come out of a wonderful *yoga nidra* straight into a heated conversation about *EastEnders*, so some soothing music can ease the transition from the tranquil to the mundane.

There are some wonderful CDs available of chants, *kirtan* and mantra, but these are not to everyone's taste. (One person's soothing ambient

86

track is another's irritating plinky-plonky.) The safe environment of a class is a good place to be introduced to this aspect of yoga, and I would encourage everyone to give it a go, even if you think it's not for you, but as with any form of music, there is good and bad. Purists would say that performers such as Deva Premal who sing rather than chant are not true to yoga, but I love her voice, and there are many other exponents in the same vein. Even so, the structure of a true Vedic chant can be very moving, and without the distraction of a tune it is easier to hone in on the words, whether that means understanding their meaning or connecting purely with their resonance; and, of course, chanting the Om, broken into three discernible syllables, A, U, M, is one of the first sounds that people thing of in a yoga context. As the *Chandogya Upanishad* proposes when contemplating on the Om: 'Verily, when he rises, he sings aloud for the sake of all creatures, to destroy darkness and fear.'

I try to engender a friendly atmosphere in classes I teach. I like my students to get to know each other and to be able to greet each other by name. I also like to keep the atmosphere light while we are working on asanas. If I say, 'How did that feel?', I love it when someone calls out, 'Fantastic!' or even 'I hated it!' However, when it comes to relaxation, concentration and meditation, the room must be as quiet as practicable.

Of the three main focuses of meditation, breath, sight and sound, perhaps sound is the most controversial. If you are looking at an object and don't like it, you can close your eyes, or if the exercise is to visualise something, you can stop any time it becomes uncomfortable. If a breathing practice becomes laboured, you can change it or let it go and allow your breathing to return to its normal rhythm.

With sound, it's much more difficult. Say the teacher puts on some gentle classical music. Lovely, but it's so easy to get wrapped up in the music on an emotional level, rather than keep your focus on the meditation practice, and if it's music you dislike, it becomes a really uncomfortable experience. I used to have a teacher who played gentle Spanish guitar music, which under concert conditions I would really have enjoyed. Somehow lying in the dark in Corpse pose changed my response and I would end up in tears every time: and I don't know why because I wasn't feeling sad before the track started. That's the power of music, I suppose. It can be very intense and stir up all sorts of feelings and emotions. This isn't necessarily a bad thing, but when it comes on unexpectedly, it can be unsettling and perhaps even embarrassing.

Alongside issues of taste and musical preference, there are practical difficulties. The volume level must be comfortable for everyone. Too loud and it might be distracting and hard to hear the teacher; too soft and it is just plain irritating. Anyone with problems with their hearing might find it particularly challenging. Also, it can exacerbate symptoms of a headache and migraine, sudden noises might startle, or there may be unpleasant vibrations.

There are other ways to bring sound to class. We can take our practice outside and listen to the sounds of nature, such as the wind, waves or birdsong, or separate elements of the class with the gentle chime of the ting-sha, or use a singing bowl. We can even tune in to the internal sounds of the body, not just the gurgling of the digestion or the rush of blood, but also those noises that the *Hatha Yoga Pradipika* describes as 'various sounds heard in the middle of the body', including an ocean, drums, bells, flute and a bee. Conversely, withdrawal of the senses leads to focus on one's inner silence.

What do you think? Should music be played during a yoga class or is it better to work in silence? If we use mantra, should we chant out loud or only in our heads? Does sound in a class become a distraction or might it serve as a reminder that we are always striving to connect with the sounds within and thence the true self?

The only way to discover whether you like music and sound in a class or prefer the silent treatment is to try it. Attend as many classes and workshops as possible, so you work with a wide variety of teachers. Experience different approaches to the use of music with an open mind and a good heart. Embrace what you like and set aside anything that is not right for you at the moment.

Peace be with you!

Breath notes

I have served my time in the massed ranks of the altos in a local choir. I wouldn't say I was a singer with a capital S, but I can hold a tune, and I loved being involved in such an uplifting community group.

At the start of every weekly rehearsal, our Musical Director would take us through some warm-up exercises to wake up our vocal cords. We'd la-la-la some scales and arpeggios, and chew imaginary toffee to get our facial muscles moving.

When the MD discovered that I was a yoga teacher, he said, 'Marvellous! How about you put us through our breathing paces next week?'

Given that some of our number were past the first flush of youth, not to mention that we stood very close together and with the gents on a step behind the ladies, it wouldn't have been appropriate to launch into Downward-facing Dog. Instead, I'd invite them to have a good shake and then stand tall in Tadasana. We'd do a few stretches to open the ribcage to give our lungs room to expand, move our bodies every which way and generally loosen up. Occasionally we'd do a sneaky Warrior stretch and often finish with a balance, which usually ended up with everyone laughing: always a good result.

It would be fair to say that this intervention did not meet with universal approval. Some choir members made their distaste clear by harrumphing their way through proceedings, with much tutting and raising of eyebrows. They clearly thought me some kind of weird hippy. One actually went so far as to refuse to join in and kept his head resolutely down in faux study of his music. There were also mumblings that the time would be better spent singing not 'doing physical jerks'. Hey ho. I'm wasn't offended. Others, though, said they really enjoyed it and during our coffee break accosted me with questions about yoga and its benefits. I love it when worlds collide.

Let silence reign in the mind

There is a perception in some quarters that yoga must be practised in total silence, or at least with nothing louder than some gentle chanting or the soft chime of a bell. Meanwhile, back in the real world, we have all manner of audible distractions to overcome.

Of course, being centred yogis, we should be able to disengage from any outside commotion. At the very least, we should use the sound as a point of focus – or perhaps chant a little louder! – but sometimes this is beyond us, and we find our attention drifting towards the kerfuffle.

I regularly teach in the upstairs room of a church, while down below the ladies' group is meeting. We get along just fine. They show forbearance when we clatter down the stairs at the end of our session, and we take advantage of the free musical accompaniment they offer. We have been treated to songs from visiting choirs and performances by hand bell ringers. There has been recorded music to accompany film shows, including one memorable instance that gave us the curious juxtaposition of Madness's 'I've Been Driving in My Car' and Freddie Mercury and Montserrat Caballé belting out 'Barcelona'. There have been some lovely coincidences, such as the time they struck up 'Morning Has Broken' downstairs just as we began our Salute to the Sun upstairs. Then again, occasionally there is a gentleman speaker using a microphone just as we roll down to relax, but we don't let it bother us. Honestly.

I've taught meditation in a community centre where in the adjacent room the Fat Fighters or some such were celebrating successes with whoops and cheers. Delighted though we were that Janice had reached her target weight, a bit of decorum wouldn't have gone amiss. I once went to a teachers' training session where we shared accommodation with a children's party, complete with an enthusiastic entertainer encouraging his audience to 'Cheer a bit louder, boys and girls!' This made most of us laugh, but there were some who didn't see the funny side at all. Really, you would expect a bit more tolerance (from we teachers, that is, not the children).

The *Upanishads* have many references to literal and metaphorical sound. We live in a noisy world, so perhaps instead of protesting that we can't concentrate, we should embrace the noise. As I write this, my son, a rock drummer, is rehearsing in the next room – and I love it.

Glossary

Here are a few simple definitions to help you make sense of the book. Images of the postures are freely available online: try, for example, yogajournal.com

ahimsa Non-violence, the first yama *See* Eight limbs

Alternate nostril breath Nadi shodhana pranayama, a practice in which the body's energy channels are balanced by directing the breath

Asana Posture or pose (pronounced as-na) *See* Eight limbs

Ashtanga Energetic style of yoga that involves synchronising the breath with a progressive series of postures (ashtanga means eight)

Bikram A branded and prescriptive style of yoga devised by Bikram Choudhury to be conducted in a very hot room

Boat Navasana

Cat Marjaryasana

Cobbler Baddha Konasana, also known as Bound Angle Pose

Cobra Bhujangasana

Cow's Head Gomukhasana, also known as Cow's Face

Crow Bakasana, also known as Crane

Dancer Natarajasana

Dolphin Makarasana

Downward-facing Dog Adho Mukha Svanasana

Dru Strong but graceful style of yoga based on soft flowing movements

Eagle Garudasana

Eight limbs Patanjali divides yoga into eight limbs or stages: *yama* (abstinence), *niyama* (observance), asana (posture), pranayama (breath control), *pratyahara* (sense withdrawal), *dharana* (concentration), *dhyana* (meditation) and *samadhi* (contemplation, absorption or super-conscious state)

Hatha Style of yoga based on the classical postures with a focus on developing and maintaining equilibrium in the forces in the body, breath, mind and spirit

Heron Krounchasana

Iyengar A disciplined style of yoga devised by B K S Iyengar that emphasises precision, alignment and quality of movement

Kirtan Style of devotional chanting: definitely not singing

Kundalini Strong style of yoga aimed at releasing untapped potential (the kundalini energy) that is envisaged as a coiled serpent at the base of the spine

Lizard Utthan Pristhasana

Locust Salabhasana

Lotus Padmasana

Mountain Pose Tadasana

Nadi shodhana pranayama see Alternate nostril breath

Namaste A gesture of greeting and respect, often translated to mean 'The divine in me acknowledges the divine in you'

Niyama See *Yama*

Peacock Mayurasana
Plough Halasana
Pranayama *See* Eight limbs
Sage's Pose Marichyasana I
Salute to the Moon Chandra namaskara (there are many versions of this sequence)
Salute to the Sun Surya namaskara (there are many versions of this sequence)
Samadhi *See* Eight limbs
Savasana Corpse Pose
Scorpion Vrschikasana
Staff Pose Dandasana
Standing Big Toe Balance Utthita Hasta Padangusthasana
Sutra Literally meaning 'thread', Patanjali's Yoga Sutras are one of the founding philosophical texts of yoga and set out its practices, approaches and expected outcomes
Tadasana Mountain Pose
Tree Vrksasana
Triangle Trikonasana
Upanishads A collection of teachings that shaped Hinduism, but have also had wider religious and philosophical influence; part of the tradition of religious literature known as the Veda
Vinyasa A series of yoga postures combined in a flowing sequence
Warrior I, II and III Virabhadrasana I, II and III
Wheel Chakrasana
Yama **and** *niyama* The first two of the eight limbs of yoga; *yama* means abstinence, *niyama* observance *See* Eight limbs

Yin Slow style of yoga in which postures are held for minutes at a time

Yoga nidra So-called yoga sleep that refreshes and restores body and mind

References

Much of the information I have gleaned over the years has come from experience and from picking the brains of my fellow teachers and students, to whom I offer my thanks. However, these are my favourite published reference sources:

Brian Dana Akers, translator, *The Hatha Yoga Pradipika*, YogaVidya.com, 2002

A C Bhaktivedanta Swami Prabhupada, *Bhagavad-Gita As It Is*, The Bhaktivedanta Book Trust, 1986

H David Coulter, *Anatomy of Hatha Yoga*, Body and Breath, 2001

T K V Desikachar, *The Heart of Yoga*, Inner Traditions International, 1995

Godfrey Devereux, *Elements of Yoga*, Thorsons, 2002

B K S Iyengar, *Light on Yoga*, Thorsons, 2001

C Jarmey, *The Concise Book of Muscles*, Lotus Publishing, 2003

Leslie Kaminoff, *Yoga Anatomy*, Human Kinetics, 2007

Juan Mascaró, translator, *The Bhagavad Gita*, Penguin Books, 2003

Valerie J Roebuck, translator and editor, *The Upanishads*, Penguin Books, 2003

Sri Swami Satchidananda, translator and commentator, *The Yoga Sutras of Patanjali*, Integral Yoga Publications, 2007

Swami Satyananda Saraswati, *Asana Pranayama Mudra Bandha*, Yoga Publications Trust, 2004

Swami Vishnu Devananda, *Meditation and Mantras*, OM Lotus Publishing Company, 1978

Louise Tucker, *An Introductory Guide to Anatomy & Physiology*, Holistic Therapy Books, 2005

About the author

Julia Thorley BWYDip has been practising yoga since she was a teenager. She teaches hatha classes and workshops in venues in Northamptonshire, including community spaces, gyms, spas and schools. She is also a writer and editor.

She may be contacted through her website www.juliathorleyyoga.com or her blog at https://yogahereswhatimthinking.blogspot.co.uk/

Other books by Julia Thorley

The Little Guide to Teaching Yoga in a Gym is available from the Amazon Kindle store
Pregnant and Fit by Sharron Davies and Julia Thorley (Partridge Press. ISBN-10: 1852252405. ISBN-13: 978-1852252403)
100 Reasons to be Confident (Four Seasons Life/Guides. ISBN-10: 1856455394. ISBN-13: 978-1856455398.)
100 Reasons to be Generous (Four Seasons Life/Guides. ISBN-10: 1856455408. ISBN-13: 978-1856455404)
100 Reasons to be Positive (Four Seasons Life/Guides. ISBN-10: 1856455416. ISBN-13: 978-1856455411)

100 Reasons to be Thankful (Four Seasons Life/Guides. ISBN-10: 1856455424. ISBN-13: 978-1856455428)
Simple Conjuring Tricks for Everyone: Learn How to Amaze Family and Friends (W Foulsham & Co Ltd. ISBN-10: 0572030606. ISBN-13: 978-0572030605)

Fiction

Scoring an Own Goal in Tennis: a short story is available from the Amazon Kindle store.
Nine Lives: Monologues and first-person stories for reading aloud is available from the Amazon Kindle store and in paperback from the author's website.
The Harmonium's Last Chord is available from the Amazon Kindle store and in paperback from the author's website.

Stripped-back Yoga